PECULIAR PETS

Amazing Poets

Edited By Wendy Laws

First published in Great Britain in 2021 by:

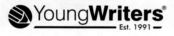

Young Writers
Remus House
Coltsfoot Drive
Peterborough
PE2 9BF
Telephone: 01733 890066
Website: www.youngwriters.co.uk

All Rights Reserved
Book Design by Ashley Janson
© Copyright Contributors 2020
Softback ISBN 978-1-80015-158-1

Printed and bound in the UK by BookPrintingUK
Website: www.bookprintinguk.com
YB0455B

★ FOREWORD ★

Welcome Reader!

Are you ready to discover weird and wonderful creatures that you'd never even dreamed of?

For Young Writers' latest competition we asked primary school pupils to create a Peculiar Pet of their own invention, and then write a poem about it! They rose to the challenge magnificently and the result is this fantastic collection full of creepy critters and amazing animals!

Here at Young Writers our aim is to encourage creativity in children and to inspire a love of the written word, so it's great to get such an amazing response, with some absolutely fantastic poems. Not only have these young authors created imaginative and inventive animals, they've also crafted wonderful poems to showcase their creations and their writing ability. These poems are brimming with inspiration. The slimiest slitherers, the creepiest crawlers and furriest friends are all brought to life in these pages – you can decide for yourself which ones you'd like as a pet!

I'd like to congratulate all the young authors in this anthology, I hope this inspires them to continue with their creative writing.

★

★ CONTENTS ★

Ocean Harrison (8)	61	Mason Herod (9)	102
Jack Wood (7)	62	Isaac Moon (9)	103
Elliott Porcas (7)	63	Amelia Lees (8)	104
Poppy Maxwell (8)	64	Connor Wright (8)	105
Maddie Jones (7)	65	Rubi Tyler (9)	106
Rosie Jackson (7)	66	Lillie-May Bingham (8)	107
Bailey Maughan (8)	67	Toby Kirk (8)	108
Naomi Robinson (7)	68	Jack Lees (8)	109
		Raj Tailor (9)	110

Moon Hall School, Dorking

		Joe Sharpe (8)	111
		Summer-Rose Bentley (8)	112
Molly Dolan (10)	69	Archie Wainwright (9)	113
Lauren Naqvi (10)	70	Tia Taylor (9)	114
Lauren Ward (10)	73	Zachary Huszarik (8)	115
Millie Blakebrough (11)	74	Ollie Spencer (8)	116
Sophie Sparks (9)	76	Marley Merriman-Scotti (8)	117
Scarlett Couzens (10)	78	Charlie Jenkins (8)	118
Alex Waugh (10)	79	Jayden Muttick (8)	119
Ellie Walford (10)	80	Alfie Rowell (8)	120
Abigail Wilson (10)	81		
Jude Verge-Nelson (10)	82		
Emily Agar (10)	83		

Uxendon Manor Primary School, Kenton

Sam Quillien (10)	84		
Freddie Lees (10)	85	Mahir Abdullahi (8)	121
Maxwell Wiffen (10)	86	Shanaia Chauhan (8)	122
Zora Ninkovic (9)	87	Ameliya Vekaria (8)	125
Siena White (10)	88	Iemima Bazgan (8)	126
Jamie Copas (9)	89	Anya Patel (8)	128
Rafferty Harding (11)	90	Priyash Patel (8)	130
Jackson Mouilah (9)	91	Sana Sadat (8)	132
Arthur Mackie (9)	92	Sophia Birsan (8)	134
		Matias Dolhascu (8)	136

St John The Baptist Primary School, Colwick

		Leeya Madhani (8)	138
		Pari Prajapati (8)	140
		Khiyani Halai (9)	142
Frazer Lee (9)	93	Hannan Hamadi (8)	144
Isla Crawford (8)	94	Zain Babar (8)	146
Lottie Hickman (8)	95	Emanuel Birsan (8)	148
Miha Karakoleva (8)	96	Suliman Daud (8)	150
Cole Cooke-Smith (8)	97	Sara Jaafar (8)	152
Ava Tomlinson (8)	98	James Carcea (8)	154
Eli-sha Lloyd (8)	99	Musa Mujadeddi (8)	156
Xander Dickerson (8)	100	Nuur Ali Abdow (8)	158
Amari Stone-Ellis (8)	101	Keshav Shah (8)	160

Mohamed Osman (8)	162
Mariam Hussain (8)	164
Taym Rammahi (9)	166
Beatrice Toader (8)	168
Aryaan Hashmi (8)	170
Sara Sas (8)	172
Yasmine-Jai Gomez (8)	174
Lavinia Boloca (8)	176
Raghavi Nanthakumar (8)	177
Sarah Bizgan (8)	178
Kieron Choo Fun Young (8)	180
Kara Lafond (8)	181
Matthew Andrade (8)	182
Roseleane Sharma Phuyal (8)	183
Timeea Ursescu (8)	184
Vera Shlyuger (8)	185
Hanif Mujaddedi (8)	186
Ayoub Aria (8)	187
Anastasia Moisii (8)	188
Sophie Soteriou (8)	189
Maria Zaghali (8)	190
Nadia Celestin (8)	191
Param Parikh (8)	192
Seja Hamid (8)	193
Mekel Charles (8)	194
Roman Shafiqi (8)	195
Irysha Savani (9)	196
Ella Gami (8)	197
Giulia Elena (8)	198
Sriraam Sivathasan (8)	199
Kamari Cunningham (8)	200
Eliza Maria (8)	201
Zakii-Ali Hussain (9)	202
Nabeel Alam (9)	203

THE POEMS

Dancing Dolphin

D olphins are beautiful creatures but...
A re a little bit crazy,
N ot calm at all.
C ould they live
I n a crazy environment? The answer is yes.
N ice they are though, but here's my story...
G ot on my way home from school and I saw...

D ancing Dolphin
O n the rock,
L ying in the sea, dancing in the
P acific, but then...
H is mum got him and he had to leave.
I was sad he had to leave, but oh well,
N othing will make me forget Dancing Dolphin.

Isla Stevenson (10)
Bargeddie Primary School, Bargeddie

The Great Monkey!

M onkey is a very nice pet.

O n Wednesdays, he gives his hat to the cat,

N ot to the rat.

K y the cat is sad because of that.

E mma does not notice that.

Y *es, why was that?* thought the rat and the cat.

Aston Jones (10)

Bargeddie Primary School, Bargeddie

Flying Fish

My flying fish made me a dish.
It tasted really nice, it had some spice.
I told him, "Your wings look good today!"
He replied, "I used some spray."
He asked if he could stay.
I said, "Yes because you're the best."

Jake Smith (9)
Bargeddie Primary School, Bargeddie

Billy The Bouncing Bunny

Billy the bouncing bunny has a coat as white as snow.
His bright blue eyes glow.
He jumps so high into the night sky.
He jumps like no other bunny can do.
When jumping he shouts, "Woohoo!"
Billy the bouncing bunny,
He is so funny.

Rachel Foot (9)
Bargeddie Primary School, Bargeddie

The Dog That Could Talk

The talking dog went for walks
And all he did was talk and talk!
His owners were so impressed,
They thought he was the best!
So for a treat,
What they did was awfully neat,
They bought him a lovely and comfy seat!

Zach Youssfi (10)
Bargeddie Primary School, Bargeddie

Flopsy The Hopping Bunny

Flopsy is a colourful bunny,
She is very funny.
She hops along and flops along.
Flopsy has a pompom tail.
She is married to a male
Who works for the Royal Mail.
What a strange thing for a bunny to do!

Ellis McKee (9)
Bargeddie Primary School, Bargeddie

The Funny Bunny

My bunny is very funny,
She's a fluffy bunny
Who loves honey.
She has a big tummy
And she also likes gummy bears.
She always bounces off of chairs
And spreads hairs.

Layla Tobin (9)
Bargeddie Primary School, Bargeddie

My Snake That Can Bake

My snake is a snake who can bake.
He made a cake.
What a very strange thing to do!
Can I get some advice from you,
About what to do...?
With my snake that can bake!

Junior Smith (9)
Bargeddie Primary School, Bargeddie

Blake The Nice Snake

My snake is called Blake.
She loves a lot of cake.
She likes rice and is very nice
But doesn't like headlice.
She loves to say hey,
Whatever the time of day.

Niamh Darroch (9)
Bargeddie Primary School, Bargeddie

Conner The Crazy Chick

He is Conner the crazy chick.
He really loves sticks.
He is really, really trendy
And is really, really friendly.
He loves to jump about
And his favourite thing is to shout.
He has got his own train
And he's got his own Boeing 747 plane.
He loves doing a live show
And loves shooting it in slow-mo.
He goes on holiday
In January, March and May.
He is Conner the crazy chick
And this is the end of his mix.

Harry Arnold (8)
Horton St Michael's First School, Rudyard

Horny-Corn

H orny-Corn and I are best friends, we swim
O r surf across huge turquoise waves,
R ock in a big hammock,
N ever argue,
Y ou and me can play with her,
-
C ome on, don't be shy,
O ver waves we go,
R ound and round in whirlpools,
N ever bored together.

Isabel Stoddart (8)
Horton St Michael's First School, Rudyard

Tomy Boy

T eleport is what he loves to do,
O lives are food he likes,
M arshmallows are good too, he does not like cactus spikes,
Y ou will love him and everyone will.

B ut when he sees cotton candy he poops out jelly beans.
O h, and he loves ice cream.
Y ou better like him or watch out!

Lillian Croft (8)
Horton St Michael's First School, Rudyard

Jerld

J erld was always bored so he used his wings to get muddy.

E ventually he got very bored of getting muddy so he decided he was going

R olling but a few hours later he got bored so he decided he was going to get a

L ollipop so he licked it all and got bored again so he

D ecided he just wanted to watch TV.

Eva-May Bloor (7)
Horton St Michael's First School, Rudyard

Super Brek

S he is a super cat.
U se cuteness to identify people.
P eople don't notice.
E ats cat food all day.
R uns like a super cat.

B e a super cat.
R un like a spy.
E at like a super cat.
K ind super cat.

Harriet Thomson (8)

Horton St Michael's First School, Rudyard

Doomzy J Is Cool

D angerous Doomzy

O ngoing rapper

O n stage he raps to millions

M aking YouTube videos every day

Z ooming around the world in his jet

Y ou've never a rapper as good as him

J ust watch him rap like you've never seen.

Monty Gardner (8)

Horton St Michael's First School, Rudyard

Super Spider

S pider is very, very cool,

P erhaps the coolest of them all,

I nside his very cool den and then he

D ecided that he was going to become cooler than

E ver, forever

R iding on his cool, amazing pets, swishing through the fast air.

Bonnie Knight (7)

Horton St Michael's First School, Rudyard

Dinestine

D inestine is my pet.

I ncredibly marvellous.

N ips sometimes.

E very single day

S noring with laziness.

T ea is his favourite drink.

I am his cuckoo creator.

N ipping you he is.

E vil genius!

Seb Richards (7)
Horton St Michael's First School, Rudyard

Graham

G raham is a really cool chick

R acing around his cage very quick

A ll day he makes lots of noise

H e plays with all of his toys

A t lunchtime he eats all of his seeds

M y mum and me give him all he needs.

Ryan Bailey (8)
Horton St Michael's First School, Rudyard

Tom The Turbo Turtle

A zoom and a flash disturbed me one day.
I was glued to the spot and as still as clay.
Then suddenly a turtle zoomed in front of me
So I climbed on and said, "Wee!"
And then, "Let me stay on I pray."

Matthew Silvester (8)
Horton St Michael's First School, Rudyard

Swizzle The Stupendous Spider

S pectacular spider
W hirling webs
I ncredible coloured legs
Z apping across the floor
Z ig-zagging up the walls
L ovely long legs
E xtraordinary eyesight.

Jasmine Wentworth (8)
Horton St Michael's First School, Rudyard

Butterfly

B lue and pink.
U tterly amazing.
T iny and bright.
T houghtful.
E xcited.
R acing.
F lying.
L oving.
Y ou will love her.

Lexi Cooper (8)
Horton St Michael's First School, Rudyard

Lucy The Fluffy Guinea Pig

L ucy is a very fluffy guinea pig.

U nlike other guinea pigs she is the most beautiful guinea pig in the world.

C ute, unique, sassy and she loves everyone.

Y ou will love her.

Rahma Al-Asbahi (8) & Sienna Bayley-Murray (8)
Horton St Michael's First School, Rudyard

Super Cool

    S o I have a pet,

Yo **U** must know his name, his name is Super

    P et, his superpower is a firebomb.

    E very day he likes to play and he

    R eally likes being trendy.

Ned Cook (7)

Horton St Michael's First School, Rudyard

Super Dog

S uper Dog has magic powers
U pside down he swings through the sky
P rotecting people everywhere
E very day he wears a blue cape
R escuing the city is his job.

Jenson Brennan (9)
Horton St Michael's First School, Rudyard

Rosie

R osie likes doing flips in the sky.
O n Saturday she flies up high.
S he is a super butterfly.
I ona is her best friend.
E very day she likes to play.

Iona Harrison (7)
Horton St Michael's First School, Rudyard

Oliver Owl

O liver Owl is amazing,
L oving and so beautiful.
I ndependent.
V icious.
E llie is his friend.
R escuing his friends forever!

Robyn Watts (7)
Horton St Michael's First School, Rudyard

Jet Pack

J agged.
E pic.
T amed.

P acked.
A n awesome alligator.
C racking creature.
K icking.

Elijah Thornton (8)
Horton St Michael's First School, Rudyard

Charlie The Cool Chick

There once was a cool chick who lived in Leek
And liked to sing from his beak.
Sometimes he liked to eat
A lot of meat
Then moved out of Leek.

Giles Ward-Banner (9)
Horton St Michael's First School, Rudyard

Pippin

P ippin

I s incredible.

P erfect peacock.

P urple, powerful peacock.

I ndigo.

N ever naughty.

Arthur Densem (9)

Horton St Michael's First School, Rudyard

Deinonychus

Deinonychus is my pet.
Roar!
He is a good pet but only eats meat at night
So he's safe in the day but not at night.
"Roar!" he says in the moonlight.
"Roar!" he says in the shed.
"Roar!" he says in Asda
But he never says roar to clowns
Or even birds, only in the moonlight.
Roar!
He has sharp teeth and claws
And he has long arms with furry blue, yellow
And orange fur everywhere.
If you're ready, join us in this amazing adventure
With your own gear,
You never know what might happen...

Logan Gowland (9)
Lingdale Primary School, Saltburn-By-The-Sea

My Flying Guinea Pig

My guinea pig wasn't as he seemed,
His sister looked at him and beamed.
I had them on my lap one day,
He flapped his ears and flew away.
Luckily he came back the next day,
While I was trick or treating in Overlook Bay.
Dumbo the Flying Guinea Pig I named him,
He looked like he was about to cause mayhem.
He looked at me and winked,
I had my eyes on him, I never dared to blink.
He gave me a smile, a little smirk
That was one of his many perks.
Making us happy every day and night,
Dumbo the Flying Guinea Pig made us happy with
all his might.

Emily Clarke (9)
Lingdale Primary School, Saltburn-By-The-Sea

Mixie The Shape-Shifter

She flies, she slithers, she slides and slides,
She hangs upside down from a gloomy cave,
She runs for miles, she is incredibly vile,
Brace yourself, or meet fate with shape-shifter
Mixie!
She has scales, she has razor-sharp nails,
She has glowing dragon eyes,
Never look directly eye to eye,
If you do, brace yourself,
Or meet fate with shape-shifter Mixie!
She has a strong scent, she has razor teeth,
She has strong ears, she has sharp antlers,
She has a snake tongue,
Beware, or meet fate with Mixie!
Beware, don't go near...

Amelia Porcas (10)
Lingdale Primary School, Saltburn-By-The-Sea

Bud My Long Dog

B eautiful like the brightest sun.
U n-amazing you can't tell.
D ependent is the way he likes it.

M ore food because he's greedy.
Y elps when he wants food.

L eaps over fences because he's clever.
O utside to dig his bones.
N ot very ferocious, not very mad.
G ood boy when he is fed.

D on't make him mad or he will be sad
O r make him very mad and he will bite you.
G o away or he will find you.

Joe Curnow (9)
Lingdale Primary School, Saltburn-By-The-Sea

Lickey Mickey

Lickey Mickey, where do I start...?
Lickey Mickey you are a licky, bucking, rearing
treat taker.
Whatever I do with you, you chuck me off.
I walk past the field and all I see is
Licky Mickey rearing and galloping over to me,
Bucking with your licky tongue.
Lickey Mickey licking my hands and face
Because he knows I have treats.
He is whining and nudging me.
"Here Mickey, my licky boy," I spoke gently.
Lickey I love you!
Lickey Mickey my 15.2hh horse.
Lickey Mickey I love you!

Grace Maughan (10)
Lingdale Primary School, Saltburn-By-The-Sea

The Sassy Snake!

The sassy snake is not mean,
She is just a show-off with her everyday outfits.
Her dad works for the Loxy Foxes,
I think that's their name.
Do you believe they have no drain?
Some days they can get really naughty.
Her dad is busy every day, they are really fussy.
Do you know what the Loxy Foxes eat?
They eat dad snakes.
Anyway to Sassy Snake,
She is always late
Maybe because of her fame.
No one knows what she does anyway.

Chloe Louise Jones (11)
Lingdale Primary School, Saltburn-By-The-Sea

A Fast Dog

I know how to spoil my dog.
Roxy catches snowballs and eats them.
She eats like a pig.
She drinks like a chicken.
She is a pig.
She walks like a penguin.
She leaps but jumps over the high ones
And lands on her feet.
She moonwalks as well.
She snores when she is asleep.
She sounds like a pig when she snores.
She fights with my other dog.
My other dog is naughty as well.

Isla Stephenson (7)
Lingdale Primary School, Saltburn-By-The-Sea

The Awful Octopus

He's ferocious, he's mean, he's vile, he's tiny.
He's slimy, he's awful, he's cruel,
He's dangerous, he's grumpy,
Prepare yourself for the awful octopus!

He's wild, he's lazy, he's messy, he's blue,
He's sassy, he's moody, he's nasty,
He's colourful, he's not tame,
Prepare yourself for the awful octopus!

Tilly Evans (10)
Lingdale Primary School, Saltburn-By-The-Sea

My Perfect Greedy Unicorn!

G reedy,

R ight to be full.

E ating unicorn food.

E verything lover.

D inosaurs were her friends.

Y ellow is her favourite colour.

U nder the sea most times.

N ever gets one portion, she gets more.

I ntelligent.

C orn lover.

O bsessed with food.

R ight to eat.

N ever full!

Caitlin Chapman (9)

Lingdale Primary School, Saltburn-By-The-Sea

The Robotic Ostrich

When I was walking home from the park,
There was an ostrich in my path.
He was wild and didn't have an owner
So I snuck him into my backyard.
However, there was a computer chip in his head
And holograms came out of his eyes.
He was a robot!
I had to run but I realised he was friendly
So I gave him a treat but he unaccepted.
However, he was my pet.

Kian Hauxwell (10)
Lingdale Primary School, Saltburn-By-The-Sea

Were Nasher

W ild Nasher at night.
E ating enormous mussels in the black night.
R ough enough to make him tough.
E ating elephants.

N ight Nasher.
A pproach with caution.
S neaking through the forest floor.
H owling at the moonlight.
E yes peeled for prey.
R oaring Nasher.

Oliver Wharton (9)

Lingdale Primary School, Saltburn-By-The-Sea

My Vicious Dog

V icious is my dog, she is
I ncredible and
C lawed and
I gnorant. She is
O bsessed with food!
U nique and
S assy to strangers.

I ndependent.
S trong.

M ajestic.
Y appy.

D oting.
O bese.
G orgeous.

Emily Coe (9)
Lingdale Primary School, Saltburn-By-The-Sea

Grumpy, Greedy German Shepherd

My dog sleeps mainly.
He eats quite daily.
He snarls and he growls
And he howls and chews the towels.
He steals bags from the cupboard
And eats food from the bin
And when we are not home
He sneaks on the sofa as well.
He's fluffy and his fur is all over the house
And he is like a soft pillow,
Trust me on that.

Maddie Davey (10)
Lingdale Primary School, Saltburn-By-The-Sea

Ferocious Ferret

Dangerous when not fed rats,
Hunts things just like cats.
Wakes up but doesn't get out of bed,
You encounter it, you're most likely dead.
I'm saying this as a warning,
So listen up because it's not boring.
If you annoy it then it will go crazy,
But I doubt it will chase you because it's so lazy.

Sonny Gowans (10)

Lingdale Primary School, Saltburn-By-The-Sea

The Dogasaur

He is a shoe muncher.
He puts on mud cream.
Non-stop talker.
He is a very silly dancer.
He does frontflips.
He does backflips.
He eats chocolate.
He drinks juice.
He is a skateboard rider,
A championship winner.
A food stomper.
Rides a bike.
Drives a Tesla model.
Drives a Lambo'.

Lucas Hauxwell (7)
Lingdale Primary School, Saltburn-By-The-Sea

The Swift Hedgehog

This swift hedgehog comes every night wanting to race,
By morning he's zooming off without a trace.
Finding his base would be a task,
So we'd better do it fast.
Searching and searching until the day's done,
Only finding he would not come.
Searching and searching, where did he go?
Did anyone know?

Noah Dennis (10)
Lingdale Primary School, Saltburn-By-The-Sea

Nancy Doodle

Nancy Doodle is a ceiling walker,
Every day she is a bit of a talker.
That sassy dog is a ballerina,
Sometimes she's a drama-rina.
When it's winter she's a rainbow pooper,
But when it's spring she's a rainbow tooter.
She goes to ice skate,
Where she makes a fantastic cake.

Darcy Morgan (8)
Lingdale Primary School, Saltburn-By-The-Sea

The Singing Lemur

She loves to sing and dance,
It is hard for her to stop.
She lives with her uncle
Who often gets put on the spot.
Her brother likes to sing but he's not so good,
He needs to practise.
Nala wants to be a millionaire like her BFF.
She loves to sing and dance.

Layla Tilley (9)
Lingdale Primary School, Saltburn-By-The-Sea

Tall Gangster Giraffe

Gangster Giraffe who is a sassy-looking creature
Likes to wear fantasy jewellery.
You know when she's around,
You get goosebumps when she is there.
Stash your jewellery before it's too late!
She is hiding in the shadows...
Beware!

Sophie Owens (11)
Lingdale Primary School, Saltburn-By-The-Sea

The Smart Starfish

My starfish,
He is smart for a starfish,
He can read
And he can count to 1,000
So he can solve any maths problem.
That's why we call him the smart jellyfish.
He can tell you the 70 times table,
He is faster than a mathematician.

Kian Rogerson (10)
Lingdale Primary School, Saltburn-By-The-Sea

Singing Staps

She sings all day and night,
She never really stops.
She is two years old,
You won't believe she is a billionaire.
She sings very sweetly,
Sometimes she dances.
She squishes the competitors like orange juice.

Rihanna Morgan (9)
Lingdale Primary School, Saltburn-By-The-Sea

The Just Chilling Cat

His big ears help him to fly,
When he flies he touches the sky.
You better watch out for the flying cat,
In the air he is like a bat.
I can see a cat in the pool chilling,
When we tell him to get out he is unwilling.

Ava Wears (7)
Lingdale Primary School, Saltburn-By-The-Sea

Daring Dinodog

Dinodog is a dancer,
When it snows he turns into a prancer.
In the night he becomes a rockstar,
Up in the attic to play his guitar.
His puffy tail helps him to fly,
Above the mountains touching the sky.

Eliza Roe (8)
Lingdale Primary School, Saltburn-By-The-Sea

Biscuit

Biscuit is a little biter but she is still cute.
She is also a monster,
She eats like one.
Biscuit is evil to me.
She has disgusting marks on her.
She is as disgusting and weird as a devil.

Olivia Gowland (7)
Lingdale Primary School, Saltburn-By-The-Sea

The Life Of The Cat

Fat cat,
Bedhead,
Rotten jumper,
Stupid cat.

Cat food,
Bed hunter,
Car crash,
Jump master.

Idiotic cat,
Dumb cat,
Riding tall,
Perched.

Lewis Jones (8)
Lingdale Primary School, Saltburn-By-The-Sea

Gircat The Giraffe And Cat

A kennings

Elephant-squasher,
Lion-friend,
Killer-teeth,
Nice-rice.

Street-master,
Gamer-tamer,
Food-gobbler,
Football-pro.

Flicks-elephants,
Fights-light.

Riley Bint (8)
Lingdale Primary School, Saltburn-By-The-Sea

Shores The Silly Shark Horse

He knows how to speak.
He knows how to ring a bell.
He knows how to talk.
He knows how to do the moonwalk.
He knows how to sing.
You just need to give him a ping.

Mia Bedford (7)
Lingdale Primary School, Saltburn-By-The-Sea

Fat Elephant

At midday, my fat pet went to sleep
And when he woke up his bed was broken.
I said, "If you break your bed you will earn a token."
He can't eat dairy.

Daiten Rogerson (8)
Lingdale Primary School, Saltburn-By-The-Sea

Bubble

B ubble, Bubble is trouble.

U nique puppy.

B ubble is a bear.

B ubble is the best.

L ovely puppy.

E ager for food.

Mia Rogerson (10)
Lingdale Primary School, Saltburn-By-The-Sea

The Dancing Dog

My dancing dog
Ate a frog.
He has brown spots
Like a log.
Smell my dog,
He smells like a frog
In a bog.
The frog was as brown as a log.

Bethany Petty (9)
Lingdale Primary School, Saltburn-By-The-Sea

Rex

He can skydive in the sky
And he's a good swimmer.
He never stops chattering.
He robs banks.
He sings loudly and quietly.
He plays Rockstars.

Joshua Coe (7)
Lingdale Primary School, Saltburn-By-The-Sea

Bobby

A kennings

Tap-dancer.
Dog-chaser.
Back-reader.
Rockstar.
Hand-biter.
Rock-eater.
Coffee-drinker.
Messy-eater.
Dangerous-teeth.

Ocean Harrison (8)

Lingdale Primary School, Saltburn-By-The-Sea

Racecar Dog

A kennings

Swim-racer,
Racecar-driver,
Jet-flier,
Big-talker.

Championship-winner,
GUI-player,
Wall-walker,
World-famous.

Jack Wood (7)
Lingdale Primary School, Saltburn-By-The-Sea

Bonnie The Wonderdog

B ites toffee.
O range puncher.
N ight hunter.
N ut nibbler.
I ceberg smasher.
E gg layer.

Elliott Porcas (7)
Lingdale Primary School, Saltburn-By-The-Sea

The Rockstar Cat

A kennings

Rockstar
Hand-scratcher
Rat-eater
Coffee-drinker
Dumbo-ears
Colourful-fur
Messy-eater
Grumpy-face
Fluffy-tail.

Poppy Maxwell (8)
Lingdale Primary School, Saltburn-By-The-Sea

The Crazy Dog

The dog is called Shadow,
He likes to eat an apple.
He likes water,
But he likes everything.
He mostly likes bananas.

Maddie Jones (7)
Lingdale Primary School, Saltburn-By-The-Sea

The Crazy Gracoon!

You better duck because she can fly.
You better run because she can drive.
She is messy and wild.
She is incredibly tall.

Rosie Jackson (7)
Lingdale Primary School, Saltburn-By-The-Sea

Rolly

R ock friend
O reo eater
L ovely licker
L avender sniffer
Y o-yo bouncer.

Bailey Maughan (8)
Lingdale Primary School, Saltburn-By-The-Sea

Lilly

L azy
I mproving
L ollipops and music
L ying
Y ellow she loves.

Naomi Robinson (7)
Lingdale Primary School, Saltburn-By-The-Sea

My Tiger

I begged and begged until I felt a bit wormish.
Then finally my dad said, "Yes," and my mum didn't
put up a skirmish.
The next day we bought her, only twenty pounds,
But my mum said her bedroom was completely out
of bounds.
That night we snuggled up in my bed
And the words came in my head as I read.
The next day we started training her so she would
be the best.
Mum said she had to be good, better than the rest.
I realised she was soppy
And loved to be with me even when I got grotty.
Mum insisted she be vegan so they would be the
same
But when Mum brought out the dinner she thought
it was a game.
But now all you know that my pet is very normal.
A tiger, of course! She makes me look very formal.

Molly Dolan (10)
Moon Hall School, Dorking

My Dog's Favourite Piddle Places

My dog's favourite piddle place is...
A door frame.
She seems to like it there.
I find it funny when my dog pees everywhere
Except my bed.

My dog's favourite piddle place is...
My dad's freshly polished black shoes,
You should see the face he pulls when he puts his
black, once-polished shoes on!

My dog's favourite piddle place is...
The toilet.
No, seriously, she literally wees in the toilet
And she's even learnt to flush the toilet!
Probably one of my favourite habits of hers.
Talk about sophisticated (for a dog at least.)

My dog's favourite piddle place is...
The bin, you heard me.

It's really annoying when she pees in my bedroom bin,
In case you haven't guessed, it's revolting.

My dog's favourite piddle place is...
The table.
I don't think I need to tell you the details about that one.
It's annoying when you watch her carelessly leave her business and not bother to tidy it up!

My dog's favourite piddle place is...
A lap.
Here is a classic prank I play on my annoying cousin.
First, I put my dog on her lap,
And my cousin is delighted
Until she feels something wet on her lap!
Works every time.

I am afraid you can't call my dog well-behaved
And certainly not easy to look after,
But she really tries her best
And all the habits above

Are different
And that's what I love
About my dog.

Lauren Naqvi (10)
Moon Hall School, Dorking

My Majestic Pet

Have you ever heard of a tigerwolfly?
Well, I have and it's my pet.
It has wings like a phoenix,
The stripes of a tiger
And its main feature is the body of an
extraordinary Arctic wolf.

At night the tigerwolfly sprouts wings from its back
And takes flight,
Its skin shimmers in moonlight,
The orange and golden wings flap silently through
the night
And the tiger stripes grow blacker.

Leaving no trace,
It runs like a bullet
And lives in my house,
The majestic animal is like no other.
Anyone would like a pet like this!

Lauren Ward (10)
Moon Hall School, Dorking

My Dog

My dog is loud, very loud.
Loud enough to wake me up in the morning.
Loud enough that the whole village can hear him
When he barks.
Oh, and definitely loud enough to scare the
postman
Out of his wits!

My dog sheds,
A lot!
My dog sheds so much
I have to hoover my room twice a day.
My dog sheds.
There isn't even one corner of the house
Where his fur isn't there.
My dog sheds so much
That once when my mum was brushing him,
I honestly thought
It was snowing!

My dog is destructive.
My dog is so destructive

That he goes through
Eleven, no sixteen footballs,
Thirty-seven tennis balls,
Three rugby balls,
One phone,
I don't know how many toilet rolls,
And well, shall I go on?

My dog is crazy.
My dog is so crazy
That when we go on a three-hour walk
He's still a crazy, lunatic dog.
My dog is so crazy
That if you leave him at home
He will have eaten the bannisters
And you're lucky if you still have your floorboards
intact.

So you see, people have dogs
That can speak French or Spanish or even Greek,
But I have my dog Duke
And I wouldn't change him for the world.

Millie Blakebrough (11)
Moon Hall School, Dorking

Ruby The Stretchy World Gymnastics Dog

Hello, my name is Ruby,
I am a sausage dog.
I love spinning around
And making a mess
But I can't stop looking cute
Because my owner said
I look cuter with a bow on my head.

My dog is stretchy
And she is the only dog with a long body
About ten foot in length.
My dog called Ruby is a gymnastic world champion
stretchy dog
She can stretch over to make a bridge
And do a flip on the bars.
She can use her stretchiness helping zookeepers
And getting birds to come back from flying away.
She is a peculiar pet,
She can do a backflip with her stretchy body
And a full twist.

My pet can do many flips that you cannot even imagine.
She is my most peculiar pet.
Ruby is so cute.

Sophie Sparks (9)
Moon Hall School, Dorking

Molly

M agical.
O bedient.
L ucky.
L oopy.
Y outhful.

Molly the magical dog was very special indeed,
She was very good most of the time but did pull on her lead.
Molly has magical glasses that she wears every day.
Everyone says, "What a cool dog, hey!"
Molly can see through all sorts of things,
From cars, doors and even bins.
Molly can see for miles and can spot anything that's there,
She likes to chase squirrels and rabbits and can run as fast as a hare.

Scarlett Couzens (10)
Moon Hall School, Dorking

My Strange Cat

My naughty cat called Billy,
Shoots people with Nerf guns for fun.
He's always up to mischief, with a smile on his face.
He hides, high up in trees and under bushes,
Ready to jump out at people.
He's as white as a sheep.
With brightly coloured eyes, he can see in the dark.
He's small, but with a big appetite like a panda.
He eats Nerf guns day and night.
He can run like the speed of light.
He's evil but not harmful.
Friendly to people without Nerf guns.
He doesn't need to sleep.

Alex Waugh (10)
Moon Hall School, Dorking

Peculiar Pets

When you go on walks
Have you seen
A snakodile?
I have.
He followed me home.
I named him Pebbles.
He's a bit nippy and spiky,
Bristly, cuddly but slimy.

He is a very hungry snakodile.
I feed him six times a day...
Pig, cow, that is pretty much it.
But he still gets treats.

His teeth are pointy
And have razors on the side of them.
I have so many cuts and scrapes from him.

Pebbles is the best pet in the world.
I could not imagine
My life without him.

Ellie Walford (10)
Moon Hall School, Dorking

Swanacorn

Out of my window, I saw a shining star,
I opened my door but it seemed so far.
To my surprise on the moonlit lawn,
Was I dreaming or is it nearly morn?

A bright blue swan, as bright as a star.
She was the most magical creature I'd seen so far,
She danced and she pranced, she twirled and she whirled
With her bright glowing horn, she smiled at me and turned.
A flick of her tail and a flinch of her head.
"What a most peculiar pet," I smiled and said.

Abigail Wilson (10)
Moon Hall School, Dorking

My Strange Shark

When I was four years old,
For some reason my mum and dad got me a vegan
shark.
I don't know why...
But we had a water tank in my back garden.

He was a baby vegan shark.
I gave him carrots, tomatoes and lettuce
And he was eating the food,
I had no idea my baby shark was vegan!

It was so cool, but when he goes in the tank
We have to clean it up for him,
It is so annoying but I still love him!
My favourite peculiar pet!

Jude Verge-Nelson (10)
Moon Hall School, Dorking

Stanley

Hi! Let me hand you over to my dog...
My name is Stanley, I will let you in on a secret...
I can dance!
I go to a secret cloud and I love to dance.
I like, no... I love to dance. Okay?
Is that okay with you?
I am going to my secret cloud.
Oh no, it is raining.
I hate rain! Noooo!
I need my raincoat and umbrella.
Okay, I am ready.
One, two, three, go!
I am here and ready to dance!

Emily Agar (10)
Moon Hall School, Dorking

Have You Seen An Elephlash?

I saw it in the desert at night,
Then I went to the sea the next day
And I got to see it once again,
It is so rare I got to see it twice
And I am 1,999 years old!

The bottom half is a gigantic elephant
And the top half is a magnificent shark,
It is as large as a megalodon
And as tall as the tallest tree in the world!
I wish I could see it again and that it could be my
pet!

Sam Quillien (10)
Moon Hall School, Dorking

My Cheeta-Rilla

He's super fast
And super strong.
He's furry and cuddly.
He's an omnivore
And super clever.
He does his business
In the toilet
And eats at the table.
He never skirmishes.
He's so cool.
We both sit on the sofa
And watch TV.
I wouldn't live without him.

Freddie Lees (10)
Moon Hall School, Dorking

The Dancing Snark

Have you ever seen a dancing snark on your
street?
I saw a dancing snark last week.
The snark was doing TikTok dances,
They were quite abysmal prances!
When he saw people looking at him,
The snark slithered down the beach,
Plunged towards the warm water
And paddled powerfully towards the pier.

Maxwell Wiffen (10)
Moon Hall School, Dorking

The Bouncing Dinoroo

I saw him last night, bouncing around the streets.
He bounced all night and all day long,
Tail wagging furiously.
He roared a terrifying roar.
I jumped in his pouch and bounced along
Until the sun went down.
Then he was gone.
Every night I look out of my window to see if he's around.

Zora Ninkovic (9)
Moon Hall School, Dorking

Llama Dog Can Dance

I saw a llama dog in the street,
Dancing his head off.
But the problem was he had a foul habit
Of spitting in the street!
Night and day he leaps and jumps
And scaled all night on buildings.
But the people need an umbrella to help
So they didn't get slimy!

Siena White (10)
Moon Hall School, Dorking

Rock Dogs

R olling at the skate park
O ld fella
C an cook
K ind

D igs in my garden
O ddest out of all
G alaxy gazer
S ings rock.

Jamie Copas (9)
Moon Hall School, Dorking

The Jedi Cat

J ungle cat
E lephants appeared out of the shadows
D rums beating
I n an odd ship

C at jumped in
A monkey growls
T he end.

Rafferty Harding (11)
Moon Hall School, Dorking

Belt The Owl Bat

Belt is a very big and scary animal.
He eats all night and drinks water,
Lazily sitting on his big chair.
Trying to tame is very hard
Because his home is at the top of a big tree.

Jackson Mouilah (9)
Moon Hall School, Dorking

Grippy Feet

G rippy feet
E nergetically running everywhere
K ind friend
P icky eater
H ealthy pet
I t's exciting
N oisy lad.

Arthur Mackie (9)

Moon Hall School, Dorking

Slothy The Silly Sloth

Slothy the silly sloth loves to hike.
You can feed him Love Hearts whenever you like.
He's a funny, silly clown.
He loves heights so he looks down.
Slothy loves to eat clouds.
He loves to sing out loud.
Slothy always has his Santa sack.
Just look at his jester hat.
He loves his clown nose.
Slothy has some spiky toes.
He only has two meals a day.
His bed is made out of hay.
Slothy lives in his big English cave.
When people walk by they give him a wave.
He always wakes up at six o'clock.
I don't know why but he has this special lock.
Slothy's skateboard swishes and swoshes.
Whenever he gets dirty he always washes.
He always wins clown medals
And that's why Slothy is so special.

Frazer Lee (9)
St John The Baptist Primary School, Colwick

Penelope The Poodle

Penelope the poodle has pink, fluffy hair.
She has a pink house which she calls her pink lair.
She is careful and kind
And she has a very sensible mind.
She is as delicate as a vase.
Once she actually flew to Mars.
She can fly as high as a bird.
When she is calm she starts to purr.
When she is tired she goes to sleep.
She's anything but a nasty creep.
When she walks her paws go tap.
Her bed is a pink, fluffy mat.
She sells candyfloss.
Her fur is as soft as moss.
She loves to play with her favourite toy.
Her body is always creeping with joy.
Her sofa is where she likes to sit.
She loves to sit down and have a good knit.
She doesn't like dog food
And is always in a good mood.

Isla Crawford (8)
St John The Baptist Primary School, Colwick

Fluffy The Bunny

Fluffy loves jumping in the clouds.
She hates bananas.
She loves bouncing on the clouds while the rainbow is out.
She eats rainbow doughnuts.
She loves singing, her voice is stunning.
She is very cunning.
She lives under the sea
And she has a mansion in the clouds
Where she goes when she goes on holiday.
Fluffy always wears a bow in her hair.
She plays the piano.
She was born in 2011.
She is eight.
She wears earrings.
She is afraid of the dark and heights.
She has a phobia of needles.
She has a phobia of wood.
She has curly hair.
She will play with any animal.

Lottie Hickman (8)
St John The Baptist Primary School, Colwick

Toffee The Rainbow Sky Tiger

Toffee the rainbow sky tiger whooshes through the wind.
She has a great mind.
She likes to be alone and she has yellow eyes
Shining like lightning.
She has pink, big, fluffy wings.
Toffee loves to do fun things.
You can feed her rainbow chicken
And give her a cup of hot chocolate
To give her a sweet treat.
Toffee lives in the sky on a giant cloud.
She does not like a crowd that's loud.
Just leave her alone or get burned
By her rainbow fire burb.
Be careful kids if you ever go on a beanstalk,
She might look cute but she will burn burp you.

Miha Karakoleva (8)
St John The Baptist Primary School, Colwick

King Kevin

King Kevin loves to roll on a mat,
Whilst chasing a delicious cat.
His eyes are bright as a volcano exploding
And I don't know what rhymes with that.
He is as cute as a mouse shining bright
But he is scared of the height.
He is the king of Doggy Land
Whilst going and getting a Nike brand.
He is as soft as a really fluffy husky
And walking up a mountain like a zusky.
He goes to pray at a church
And going on YouTube and getting some merch'.
He lives in a castle very modern
And now it's very golden.

Cole Cooke-Smith (8)
St John The Baptist Primary School, Colwick

YoungWriters Est. 1991

Willmot The Dog

Willmot the dog can ride a horse.
He can drive a Lamborghini.
He has a blue house
And lives with a mouse.
He wears a tutu
With a black and blue leotard and ballerina shoes.
He sings like Katie Perry
And plays the guitar while doing the cello.
His fur is as soft as a silk blanket.
He juggles in the jungle.
He hypnotises people whenever he feels like it
And only eats chocolate.
He is a mighty strong man
And sleeps on a cloud.
He can fly and he can talk.

Ava Tomlinson (8)
St John The Baptist Primary School, Colwick

Browny The Hero!

Browny the hero can do kung fu.
She likes noodles, they might be new.
Her claws are like a razor
But her eyes are like a laser.
She is quite tough
Her skin is very rough.
She eats grilled chicken.
On the stairs she likes sitting.
She rolls down the stairs like a pear.
When the door knocks she has no fear, she growls
and looks like a bear.
She eats from the table
But she likes going to see Grandma Mabel.
She sings like Sleeping Beauty
and likes watching movies.

Eli-sha Lloyd (8)

St John The Baptist Primary School, Colwick

Flying Fish Called Floppy

There is a fish called Floppy who is not rude.
You can feed him but only fish food.
He is the authority of a spy agency.
He is really important, even though he is three.
Floppy has a helmet that is black and green.
Sometimes he does like to be mean.
He flies through the clouds and sees lots of birds,
All of them like to read blurbs.
He has a friend that is called Scwog,
Scwog lives in a bog.
Floppy flies to Scwog's bog every day,
All he does is say hey.

Xander Dickerson (8)
St John The Baptist Primary School, Colwick

Robby The Robot Rabbit

Robby the robot rabbit is half fluffy and half metallic.
Robby loves to ride on her wheels.
She can pull a sword out of her metallic arm.
She hates Peppa Pig and the colour blue.
She drinks oil but doesn't eat anything.
Her arms are half fluffy and half metallic.
Her legs are half fluffy and half metallic.
She lives in a science lab.
Her voice sounds like a distorted, squeaky robot.
Her house is made out of metal.

Amari Stone-Ellis (8)
St John The Baptist Primary School, Colwick

Bone Wings Raccoon

He is a rocket.
He loves being a rocket.
Bone Wings Raccoon eats bones.
He lives in a rock house
And sometimes out in the woods.
He can rock, he can be fun.
Bone Wings Raccoon hates dogs.
He has a guitar and guitar eyes.
Bone Wings Raccoon's arms are bone arms but fluffy.
Bone Wings Racoon's legs are bone legs but furry.
His voice is like a rocket and a rapper.
His mic is as hard as a rock.

Mason Herod (9)
St John The Baptist Primary School, Colwick

Doug The Dog

Doug the dog loves to play with toys.
He only likes boys.
He hates girls.
He lives in a mansion.
He only follows me.
He doesn't leave me.
He feeds me.
I feed him.
He hates Mollie.
He loves Mummy.
He loves Daddy.
He likes watching me playing Fortnite.
I take him on a walk.
He likes to eat pork.
He likes to go on a walk.
He only likes adult girls.

Isaac Moon (9)
St John The Baptist Primary School, Colwick

Sky The Dog

Sky the dog has a beautiful song.
She likes to eat strawberries and berries, yum, yum.
Her voice is too lovely and sweet.
Sky hates rice.
She smells like flowers.
She lives in her sister's bedroom.
Her eyes are like a sparkling disco ball.
She also runs like a train.
Her teeth are like a white flower.
Her legs are like a jumping frog.
Her bark is like a yelling teacher.

Amelia Lees (8)
St John The Baptist Primary School, Colwick

The Neon Dragon And The Rhymes

Fire the dragon likes a little nap
While having a cat.
He eats boxes and foxes.
He will eat a bit of meat
For a little treat.
Fire likes Dier.
He has eyes as bright as a pouncing wolf.
He is as deadly as a cobra.
He flies as fast as a griffin.
He has teeth and he likes wheat.
He wades and he wades.
He's from India
And he likes reindeer.

Connor Wright (8)
St John The Baptist Primary School, Colwick

Deepsea Dragon

Deepsea Dragon is as fast as an eel.
You can feed her blueberries whenever you like.
She likes to swim with the dolphins.
She has long thin wings.
Her claws are webbed like fins.
She lives underwater but she can fly.
Sometimes she goes into the sky.
She lives in an ice cave.
Her favourite food is ice berries.
She loves playing in the coral.

Rubi Tyler (9)
St John The Baptist Primary School, Colwick

Coco The Dog

She loves cabbage with soup.
She can juggle with knives.
She lives on a lamp post.
Her arms are curly noodles.
Her eyes are like fire.
She has a bit of fear.
Her legs are like a giraffe's.
She is giant.
She is as strong as a bull.
Her paws are as big as an elephant.
Her ears are as delicate as glass.
She hates dog chews.

Lillie-May Bingham (8)
St John The Baptist Primary School, Colwick

Rocky The Dog

Rocky the dog,
He loves drumming.
He lives in a mansion.
He likes sweets and treats.
He hates meat but he likes treats.
He plays on a mean drum
While he's chewing some gum.
He has eyes as dark as the night
And he had a fright.
He has sunglasses as bright as the sun.
He has spiky hair
And he's always fair.

Toby Kirk (8)
St John The Baptist Primary School, Colwick

Sky The Dog

Sky the dog can eat her dinner with a knife and
fork.
Her eyes are like lightning.
She had a bit of a frightening.
Her ears are like a goblin's.
She like hopping
And robbing.
She likes the popping of the popcorn.
Her legs are like lasers
But she has a razor.
She is rough.
She went to India
And saw a reindeer.

Jack Lees (8)
St John The Baptist Primary School, Colwick

Mickey Monkey

Mickey Monkey is a monkey.
He lives in the Amazon rainforest.
He eats honey
And has lots of money.
Mickey Monkey hates wearing clothes
But likes hugging his pillows.
His legs are really brown.
His voice is as funky as a monkey.
He can jump higher than a mansion.
He likes to run around the rainforest.

Raj Tailor (9)
St John The Baptist Primary School, Colwick

The Best Beaver

One fine day my pet Coco the brown beaver
Rode a fluffy bike.
He lives in a secret room in my house.
You can feed him chicken nuggets
But he will sing you a long song.
He loves volcanoes
But in the end, he will become a Polcano.
Then it will be chaos.
He hates tarantulas
But he can fly.

Joe Sharpe (8)
St John The Baptist Primary School, Colwick

Princess Rose

She is a hamster.
She loves bedtime.
She can eat beef.
She hates cats.
She eats magical food.
Princess lives on a bed.
Her house is metal.
Princess' legs are little.
Her eyes go like a disco ball.
Princess' eyes water like the wonderful taps.
Her fur is so fluffy.

Summer-Rose Bentley (8)
St John The Baptist Primary School, Colwick

The Mixed Animal

He can do the Irish dance.
He loves Archie W, lions and wolves.
He hates the moonlight.
His voice goes *ggonikoinkquauwoof*.
His arms are like the wheels of a Lamborghini.
He eats magic.
He was born on 17th November 2011.
His age is eight.
He has shiny solar panelled wings.

Archie Wainwright (9)
St John The Baptist Primary School, Colwick

Gilly The Ginger Giraffe

Gilly the ginger giraffe eats long noodles.
He hates poodles.
He loves trains.
He rides the plains.
He can fly.
He can't say bye.
He lives in India.
He can't fly a reindeer.
He is shy,
Now he can say bye.
He goes to Mars.
He eats Mars bars.

Tia Taylor (9)
St John The Baptist Primary School, Colwick

Magneto The Technology Scorpion

He zooms like a burning bullet.
He changes technology to zoom and cause trouble.
He goes in the shadows to be invisible
And to say hi.
When he is sad he goes blue.
He can pretend to be a human.
To make him zoom you have to be green.
He will zoom like crazy.

Zachary Huszarik (8)
St John The Baptist Primary School, Colwick

Lava Dragon

Lava Dragon goes in the trees
And always has fleas.
He flies in the sky
And he goes very high.
He lives in a hot cave
And there was a lava wave.
He eats a hot treat
And it is as big as a car.
He flies in the sky
And never says bye.

Ollie Spencer (8)
St John The Baptist Primary School, Colwick

Flames The Fighter Fish

Flames the fighter fish is hotter than a volcano.
He's as deadly as a Burmese python.
His eyes glow like a wolf at night.
His scales glow on a full moon.
He dives faster than the speed of sound.
He lives in a cave.

Marley Merriman-Scotti (8)
St John The Baptist Primary School, Colwick

Texas The Burrowing Hippo

Texas has a pet peregrine falcon.
He also has a bull shark army.
His home is a burrow.
He is a cunning hippo looking for fish.
His favourite thing to do is climbing.
His favourite food is salmon.

Charlie Jenkins (8)
St John The Baptist Primary School, Colwick

Danny The Tarantula

Danny the tarantula can fly in the air.
Her fangs are as sharp as razor blades.
Her eyes are as black as night.
Danny is a superhero.
She can hypnotise everybody
And can juggle.

Jayden Muttick (8)
St John The Baptist Primary School, Colwick

Rocky The Cat

Rocky the cat rides a bike.
He is afraid and cries when he sees mice.
He eats chicken.
His eyes glow like a lightning strike.
He hugs lots
And plays with rocket Lego.

Alfie Rowell (8)
St John The Baptist Primary School, Colwick

Danny The Dog

Danny the dog has wonderful hair,
He searches for scrumptious food everywhere.
It seems to him nobody even cares.
So he tries to be alert and aware.
Well, five little kids give him a very hard glare.

"Let's go to the weird, crazy place.
Everybody goes because there is snow."
He orders a Slushy and cake for dessert,
Waits near the tall metal pole.
He goes to the bumper cars
Because he wants to be out of control!

Danny's superpower is super lasers,
Right from his eyes, the size of a pinrole
Danny's other superpower is every time he
breathes
A huge amount of fire comes out of his mouth
whole!
Danny's final power is turning into different
animals with his own soul!

Mahir Abdullahi (8)
Uxendon Manor Primary School, Kenton

Georgina Giraffe

The day that I woke up and saw the cutest baby
giraffe,
I felt like I really needed to laugh!
As soon as I saw the giraffe, I wanted to keep it,
So I thought I'd train it so it gets fit.

Georgina Giraffe at school,
She is very, very nice,
Though the others are sometimes cruel,
She'll do anything, no need to ask her twice.

She has a favourite hobby,
She is happy because she has a friend called
Dobby.
For lunch Georgina loves boiled eggs
And she loves them best with freshly baked bread
from Greggs.

Georgina Giraffe at school,
She is very, very nice,
Though the others are sometimes cruel,
She'll do anything, no need to ask her twice.

Do you know Georgina's biggest, greatest fear?
When she sees them she cries out tears,
Dark blue is the colour of Georgina's beautiful blue eyes,
Sometimes Georgina tells a few lies.

Georgina Giraffe at school,
She is very, very nice,
Though the others are sometimes cruel,
She'll do anything, no need to ask her twice.

Now I think I should send Georgina to school,
She came home and told me the others were cruel.
The next day she hung her coat on a peg,
For lunch, there was not one egg or freshly baked bread from Greggs.

Georgina Giraffe at school,
She is very, very nice,
Though the others are sometimes cruel,
She'll do anything, no need to ask her twice.

Her handwriting is really bad, so she tries,
She can't do it yet so she cries.

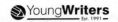

I bought her some new shoes but they were not her size,
She never ever wears any ties.

My peculiar pet is so odd,
A giraffe who goes to school.

Shanaia Chauhan (8)
Uxendon Manor Primary School, Kenton

Cat Dahl

He is the greatest writer of all.
He will write until he is the best of them all.
He's the guy that will always get brighter.
Let's all hang his writing up on the wall.

Call him night or day,
He will be there like you say.
Just give him a chair or a pear,
Or he won't be there.

Last week he won a book fair,
With the money he bought a pear and a chair
That led to a nightmare.

If you look in his eyes,
You can tell that he's wise.
He really wants to win a prize.

You can tell he's been alive for years,
By the look of his ears.
And you can tell he can be fierce,
If you touch his ears.

Ameliya Vekaria (8)
Uxendon Manor Primary School, Kenton

Pancake In Space

Pancake the pigeon has a short nose.
His cheeks are as red as an English rose.
Pancake the pigeon has absolutely no hair
But she has soft wings that come in a pair.
Pancake the pigeon has eyes like the sunrise,
But the size is as big as a winning prize.
Pancake the pigeon has miniature ears,
As he flies he can hear a lot of cheers.

Oh!
He's great,
He's eight, he's number one,
He's full of joy
With many toys.

Pancake has arrived in space,
Dun, dun, dun!
He started his journey in Mars
And bought a massive jar.
He flew around with his epic rocket wings to start his adventure.
Rocks came at him and he used his eye lasers to destroy them!

Wow!
He's great,
He's eight, he's number one,
He's full of joy
With many toys.

Pancake's powers are full of might.
He has lasers shooting out from his eyes.
He has an inventing bag which is helpful indeed.
He has an invisible computer that only he can see.
He has rocket wings that can blast in space.

Oh!
He's great,
He's eight, he's number one,
He's full of joy
With many toys.

Iemima Bazgan (8)
Uxendon Manor Primary School, Kenton

Dexter The Dove

Dexter the dove has lovely, soft feathers all
around,
His eyes are like diamonds with white sparks and
the colour of the sunrise.
Short, but skinny legs like sharpened pencils
And his lips, no lips but a beak
That's the same colour as his fingertips.
His rosy cheek show through his creamy feathers,
He has lasers that are bright orange like the
blazing, shining sun.

Dexter goes to shop for groceries in Sainsbury's,
He grabs a basket and flies up to the roof.
Then lands on the moving conveyor belt.
He sits in the basket and goes down,
Grabs a coffee, a sandwich and a chocolate bar,
Then he talks to a lady and asks if he could sit in a
huge trolley,
With blankets and pillows in it and be pushed by
her really fast around the whole shop.

His lasers are amazing,
He uses them for warming up food.

He wanted a pot of macaroni cheese so he used
his lasers to warm it up.
It was indeed yummy
But he wanted something else.
Warm milk and cookies were the answer
So he used his magnificent lasers to warm it up
And it was sooo yummy!
Dexter the dove had a great day.
Now it is time to sleep though

Anya Patel (8)
Uxendon Manor Primary School, Kenton

Baa Baa Sheep And The Chocolate Factory

Baa Baa Sheep went shopping,
Can you guess what is in his basket?
Chocolate, chocolate, and chocolate.
Today is the day for different shapes of chocolate.

Today's favourites are square, triangle
And rectangle.
Next shapes are cylinder, hexagon
And pentagon.

All yummy chocolates for Baa Baa Sheep.
I wish Baa Baa Sheep could share with us.

Oh, I wonder how it tastes.
Strawberry, apple, caramel, banana, potato,
Tomato and ice cream.

I really think it tastes like every flavour...
I can't handle it.
Please Baa Baa Sheep just one thing I ask for...

Home time!
A sheep's worst time of day if I say so myself.

All the shops with chocolate close down.
Everyone goes home,
The shops are closed.

Finally, Baa Baa Sheep goes home with anger.
He gobbles all the chocolate like it's nothing
And says, "I want more chocolate."

Chocolate, chocolate and chocolate all day,
I hope he changes.
This is the peculiar pet that likes to eat too much
chocolate.
Please Baa Baa Sheep can you stop eating
chocolate?

Priyash Patel (8)
Uxendon Manor Primary School, Kenton

Meow Highness

Listen to our brightest queen of all,
She'll always be loyal,
If she's on a roll,
Then all of you bow to our Queen of Royal.

I say it's true because she's the Queen of
Brightness,
There's nothing to do to beat the queen.
She's the Highness, she lives near the Gates of
Lightness,
She has nothing to do so she'll literally lean.

Meow Highness has a crown shimmering with
handfuls of money,
She has diamonds worth everything
Her amazing crown is surprisingly made out of
gold honey,
Sorry, but you compared to her is nothing.

My fab pet gets dresses that you'll never find,
She always gets invited to The Pet Stars,
But she declines, she doesn't want to wear her
dresses

And make you blind,
She's just too kind and gets gazillion glittery cars.

Meow Highness has her own pet called Fresh
Whitney,
He is just so nice,
All of Meow Highness' pets are so fit.
Whitney's only weakness is loving mice!

My peculiar pet, Meow Highness is my dream pet,
I bet she is the right pet.

Sana Sadat (8)
Uxendon Manor Primary School, Kenton

Catarina The Ballerina

Every time, when you see her, she is very dancy.
She's a multimillionaire,
Like people in France!
And rich money falls out of the air, air, air.

This ballerina is really funny,
If she trips she wouldn't care.
And she's as sweet as chocolate bunnies,
She always sits on princess chairs!

She loves dancing with teddy bears,
She dances with whipped cream,
Doesn't even care!
She makes dancing teams.

She the best at (real) dancing,
Loves dancing in front of the town.
Loves travelling in a trance
And loves dancing in front of all bands.

She loves wearing fancy hats!
It's so nice when you see her wiggling around.

She's a very pretty cat.
"I love dancing with the ground!"

Catarina the ballerina loves ballet too!
Well, I am surprised!
She loves teddy bears
And she loves pies!

There's never been a peculiar pet like her I bet.
Catarina the ballerina is the most peculiar pet
ever.
She even has a jet.

Sophia Birsan (8)
Uxendon Manor Primary School, Kenton

Mr Big Boxing

He's the best boxer of them all,
He'll beat a great big old bull,
Get him angry and he'll put a hole in a wall,
Yet he's still the coolest of them all.

Mr Big Boxing thinks he's a multimillionaire,
But he never says he's a winner to be fair!
People say he's a legend of boxing life,
He's never going to punch little mice.

In one punch a rhino is put down,
But why is it a rhino instead of a dino?
Don't look in his eyes he'll make you jump like a
dice,
But why him if he's scared of mice?

He's never eaten an apple pie,
But people think it's just a lie.
There's no big old lie about that!
It's the reason that he's hugely fat!

Never tell him any lies,
He'll make you take off like flies.

Tell him he's a champion
So he can feel he has won!

Mr Big Boxing is my favourite peculiar pet,
He's someone who you'll never forget!

Matias Dolhascu (8)
Uxendon Manor Primary School, Kenton

Hacking Hamster's Hobbies

Hacking Hamster is plump and short,
He has fluffy silk hair.
At night his dark blue eyes stare,
His ears, his long pink ears can hear miles away.
Hacking Hamster's sharp razor teeth
Shine when he smiles,
He's full of glee,
When he laughs, it sounds very mean.

Hacking Hamster loves to skip,
While eating a lot of chips.
He likes to climb the Eiffel Tower
And shows off his superpowers.
He likes to climb a tree,
Without hurting his knee.
Every year he bursts into tears
Because he has to cheer.
He goes to the park and makes some friends,
Then he says, "I don't want to see you again."

Hacking Hamster can fly very high
And he does exercise at sunrise.
When he's mad firebolts
Shoot out of his hands.
He can hack any gadget
But his main superpower is that he can turn
invisible
And that's the way he likes it,
Because no one knows he's in disguise.

Leeya Madhani (8)
Uxendon Manor Primary School, Kenton

The Snake Who Went To McDonald's

Hair, hair, she has no hair.
She absolutely couldn't be bare.
Legs, legs, she has no legs,
Slithering around she begs and begs.
Claw, claw, she has no claw,
Soon she will make a law
Nose, nose, she has no nose,
Now she's mad so she wants a rose.

Spooky, scary snake, spooky, scary snake,
Spooky, scary snake,
The spooky, scary snake who went to McDonald's.

She slithered to McDonald's and by the end of the day,
She slithered to the person and morphed into a human
And said, "I want a burger, chicken nuggets,
An ice cream and a bucket of clay."
She finished her food and started to paint,
Whilst turning back into a snake.

Spooky, scary snake, spooky scary snake,
Spooky, scary snake,
The spooky, scary snake who has powers.

Her powers went crazy, she kept on dying
And turning into clay, that is grey.

Pari Prajapati (8)
Uxendon Manor Primary School, Kenton

Starving Meow

She's the hungriest kitty of all!
She'll be selfish and eat all...
Also never shares at all!
Never go near her or you'll fall.

She'll eat your food!
While she's in a bad mood.
She'll only share...
With her teddy bear.

She'll find pigeons that fly in the yard
And then she'll eat the pigeons in the junkyard.
When she wears my dress she'll go blind,
No offence kitty!

When she goes to pet school...
She is such a fool.
Then she'll run out of pet school!
So then I make a search party!

She always makes such a pity!
She's such a good kitty.

It's so cute when she looks into my eyes,
She wants food so I make a surprise.

Starving Meow is my peculiar pet,
I bet you won't ever find this pet.
So stay away from my cat
Or I'll hit you with my bat.

Khiyani Halai (9)
Uxendon Manor Primary School, Kenton

My Peculiar Pet

My peculiar pet who came to me,
She likes bubbles and ice and sweet lemon tea.

She always has a lovely big smile
That's as long as a mile.

My peculiar pet, my peculiar pet,
Oh my peculiar pet,
My peculiar pet who gets into trouble
And runs half a mile.

My peculiar pet she is lovely and pink,
As cute as she looks she really is trouble
And like I said runs half a mile.

My peculiar pet who likes to run
And while she runs she has lots of fun.

My peculiar pet, my peculiar pet,
Oh my peculiar pet,
My peculiar pet who gets into trouble
And runs half a mile.

My peculiar pet, my peculiar pet,
Sweet, soft, cuddly, madly cute
With pink bows in her hair
Which I have not said.

Her fur is white, as fluffy as can be,
She's a small, cute puppy as cute as can be.

Hannan Hamadi (8)
Uxendon Manor Primary School, Kenton

Super Cat

He's the greatest superhero of all,
He will be the best amigo of them all.
Always there when you call,
All cheer for our hero!

Every day he worked so hard,
Saving the civilians near and far.
He goes to save the planet alone.
The world is saved, just call his phone!

Last week he saved an old man from falling,
He saved him from calling... 999.
The poor office man dropped his mail,
Super Cat came, he never fails at all.

Super Cat loves to hear his people's cheers,
Super Cat helps the people on his planet with their
fears.
Don't panic, he will always be there,
He will always help his people indeed!

Super Cat wears a flashy cape that looks dodgy,
His hobbies are to help his people indeed.

Super Cat loves to help his people as a hero,
He is always a helpful hero!

Zain Babar (8)
Uxendon Manor Primary School, Kenton

My Guinea Pig

My guinea pig who came to live with me had a smile
As long as a mile.

My guinea pig, my guinea pig, he has a smile
As long as a mile.

His name is Mike
And he rides his bike.
He rides it near
And he rides it far.

My guinea pig, my guinea pig, he has a smile
As long as a mile.

His hair is grey
So everybody gets out of his way.

My guinea pig, my guinea pig, he has a smile
As long as a mile.

My guinea pig, his friend is a bird
Who knows every word.

It even has a rose
Instead of a nose.

My guinea pig, my guinea pig, he has a smile
As long as a mile.

My guinea pig he has a friend who can't even see,
A bee who is stealing her key.

My guinea pig, my guinea pig, he has a smile
As long as a mile.

Emanuel Birsan (8)
Uxendon Manor Primary School, Kenton

The Bird Who Ruined The Football Match

Bubbles is a bird who is very colourful.
Bubbles is going to pop the football
And hear it pop with his ears and cheer.
Bubbles has been here last year.
Bubbles has lips and hips.
Bubbles has a nose and elbows.

Bubbles is going to land on people and disturb them.
Someone is eating a date on a plate
And Bubbles snatches it off.
Bubbles is sad because people say, "Go like a crow."
Bubbles soon sees people coming out.
The people are shouting, "Witch hunt!" Bubbles hears
And then his eyes are full of tears.
When he goes to the ground he scores for a team.
The team are surprised.

Bubbles' superpower is that he can eat anything,
Even a tall building.
He can fly to a different country and not get tired.
His last superpower is he can turn into anyone.

Suliman Daud (8)
Uxendon Manor Primary School, Kenton

My Little Hamster

My peculiar pet came to me,
To see the ocean sea.
His favourite food is pies, not bees.

How cool is he?
How cool is he?
How cool is he?

His birthday is in June.
His dream is to go to the moon.
His date is eight.

How cool is he?
How cool is he?
How cool is he?

His hair is like a flare,
Fluffy like cotton fur,
He has small, cute paws sharper than jaws.

How cool is he?
How cool is he?
How cool is he?

He's leaving now,
Please stay.
He will for a day,
Now he is eating prunes with a spoon?

How cool is he?
How cool is he?
How cool is he?

When I saw his beautiful eyes,
I jumped out in surprise.
When he was scared he ate a pear.
He shed many tears,
To show his fears.

Sara Jaafar (8)
Uxendon Manor Primary School, Kenton

The Dog That Messed Up Dubai

Sam the dog had wonderful hair.
He searches all around for a pear.
He found a paw of a catfish.
He runs super fast enough.
He is very strong like a tree
But Sam got a huge penalty fee.
He is being very good and caring,
Listening to his owner and staring.

One time he went to Dubai,
To Burj Kalifa,
He likes to jump off the Burj Kalifa
With a parachute
Like a flare.

In the soft light air
Sam bought a room.
He went to the toilet and collected toilet paper
And then he destroyed his room.
But then he had superpowers.

He was shooting laser eyes.
He was the very first.
Soon to burst.
Soon he shot fire from his mouth.
He had a sheet
And all that merriment was a treat.
He could try to go invisible
And it worked.

James Carcea (8)
Uxendon Manor Primary School, Kenton

The Cat Chef

My cat's name is Nate Nathan.
He is full of anger.
His job is gone.
My cat's nose is more colourful than a rose.

His hair is orange and white.
He is very furry and warm.
His claws are in his paws.
He got bitten by a bear
And he can't bear the sadness.

He is near you and you can hear his purr.
The cat is going to a restaurant to have a new job.
His eyes are blue and he cries, his eyes are wise.
Beware he is going to the restaurant.

He chops chicken by throwing knives,
He grills chicken by shooting lasers.
He can wash his hands fast,
Also, he can cut fast.
He can hold 100kg.
He will make his food to give out to the restaurant.

My pet's superpower is shooting lasers from his eyes and arms,
Also he can fly.

Musa Mujadeddi (8)
Uxendon Manor Primary School, Kenton

Pilot G

This pilot is extremely funny,
Every passenger isn't really safe at all.
He does it for the money.
His plane may crash and tumble.

You can see him in the private lounge,
A very famous celeb' pilot he is,
But he needs a rest while hanging in the lounge.
How can he fly without anyone?

Everyone gasps!
He may be a goat
But he has an important task
Which is not to drive a boat.

He's an extremely chilled goat
But hates cold nights when he flies.
He originates from a grassy hill,
His licence to fly isn't old!

He used to be an amateur at flying,
But everyone is disguised.

He's now not an amateur at flying.
His company is Hingiusiel.

Pilot G, the most peculiar pet
You'll ever meet.

Nuur Ali Abdow (8)
Uxendon Manor Primary School, Kenton

Hocking Kangaroo

The best hockey player in town!
He hops around just like a clown.
He has been the best hockey player!
If you scare him he won't show any fears.

He is a multimillionaire,
He always likes to share.
Hocking Kangaroo is very kind,
He always thinks first using his mind.

He has never ever lied.
Has he ever cried?
One of his hobbies is hopping,
Though he hates mopping.

He sees some people that beg
While he goes to hang his clothes with pegs.
He likes to eat boiled eggs,
Though he eats with his legs.

He likes to play hockey
Though he plays down the lobby.

He likes to have some fresh air,
He thinks it makes the game fair.

Hocking Kangaroo is my peculiar pet,
Nobody will be better than him I bet.

Keshav Shah (8)

Uxendon Manor Primary School, Kenton

Gucci The Spider With His Lambo'

Gucci the spider has big eyes.
He is very excited for a big prize.
He has no hair
But he likes to get fresh air.
He has long and big legs
But he never has to beg.
He has a rough and spiky cheek
And he crawls up to people's feet.

Gucci the spider was riding his Lambo',
In June he bought a new mansion.
When he was driving, his hair
Was flying around in the air.
He has very sharp claws.
Razor teeth on his jaws.
Gucci the spider made a hole.
His bowl was rolling outside
And he stopped it with his claw.

Gucci the spider has superpowers.
His superpowers are to shoot someone
And he can turn into the person.
He is very brave.
He could save the world.
He is a boy
Who loves playing with toys.

Mohamed Osman (8)
Uxendon Manor Primary School, Kenton

Purr...ina

Purr...ina is the best dancer of all,
For sure she will beat you.
She is oh so very tall,
She's better than you all.

She is always very funny,
You can tell she will win, no doubt.
She really likes honey,
She is never lazy on the couch.

She sticks to every rule,
She is always in the mall.
Her dress is very outstanding,
She never misses a landing.

In ten seconds she's here and there,
Give her a kitten and show you care.
She hates sports, loves only ballet.
Her birthday is in May so you shall pay.

Take her on a date, she will be your music.
She will show you tons of tricks.

Give her a flick.
Take her on a walk and she will be dancing.

Mariam Hussain (8)
Uxendon Manor Primary School, Kenton

DJ Dino

DJ Dino is the greatest DJ,
He shouts out loud,
He DJs in his PJs,
There's always a big crowd.

During the day DJ Dino
Will shout and sing.
He plays with Rhino
And Rhino says, "Bling, bling."

He is really slim.
He only has one best friend.
Trust me, try to be friends with him!
But his DJ times are going to end.

If you hang out with him all he will do is play on his
deck,
He loves being a DJ
But he can still wreck.
He buys lots of stuff from eBay.

If you give him a crown
He will be happier than ever.

He is not brown,
But he eats a lot of leather.

DJ Dino is the best peculiar pet.
I hope you like him.

Taym Rammahi (9)
Uxendon Manor Primary School, Kenton

Gi Fabulous

She's the greatest girl of all
You don't have time to see her fall
She's a stunning queen of make-up
The only thing she won't forget is
Her little dance called the shake up

Gi Fabulous, believe me or not
She takes one hour to do a knot
Now she is star writer
And seems to be brighter

She tries to be wise
But always cries
She wants to give some shine
And so she's never in time

Gi Fabulous is always late
So you never want to have a date
Whevever you call
She will be at the ball

She's undeniably pretty
She's always in a dash

She's automatically a fitty
It's clear she is a fash.

Beatrice Toader (8)
Uxendon Manor Primary School, Kenton

Splash Splat Mittens

He always splashes.
He'll always win!
He dashes to the finish line!
He'll always take a calming swim.

People say he's cool!
Others say he's a fool!
Sometimes he lies
But he's very wise.

He'll always get cheers!
He's been swimming for years!
He'll give you advice on how to dash.
He always does a big splash!

He can be very funny.
He really likes his money.
He's undeniably great.
He's my best mate.

He loves to eat for a break.
The cat who eats.
The cat who eats a Greggs.

He is the best peculiar pet
And I bet he's the best pet in the world.

Aryaan Hashmi (8)
Uxendon Manor Primary School, Kenton

Jumpy The Jumping Sheep

She helps me crash and jump,
It's amazing how she does that, *bash*.
Just watch how she does that big bump,
There's a big lump when she does a splash.

When she jumps it looks like she flies,
She is so wise.
She jumps like birds flying in the sky,
It's amazing how she tries.

She's my best friend of all,
She helps me make cash.
She's by my side whenever I call,
She gets there in a flash.

She has small ears,
She has fluffy hair,
She has practised for years,
She wins fairs.

She likes to eat eggs,
She likes to fly in a jet,
She even eats Greggs,
She is my best peculiar pet.

Sara Sas (8)
Uxendon Manor Primary School, Kenton

The Hamster That Stole Some Food

The hair of Oreo's
Fur is black and white.

To hide in a dark space
He's softer than a furball.

His eyes are black
And dark like coal.

The hamster likes to jump,
Roll and climb.

Oreo's legs are as small as a sofa's leg,
On his paws, he has sharp claws,
They are like a shark's teeth.

His ears are as small as a tooth,
You think he can't hear with them
But he can hear with them.

The cheeks of the hamster are soft like a rose
But he has no elbows!

His superpower is seeing through walls,
Lasers coming out of his eyes.
Fire coming out of his small mouth.

Yasmine-Jai Gomez (8)
Uxendon Manor Primary School, Kenton

Cupcake The Dove

Cupcake the dove has a small nose
And has a medium neck that grows.
She has white feathers that she flies with.
Cupcake's eyes are a sparkly dark prize.
Her legs are long and bare.
Cupcake has colourful feathers but no hair.

Her eyes are dark like chocolate.
Her feathers are white as a blanket.
Her cheeks are cute and beautiful.
Her ears are good at listening.
Cupcake's toes are soft like a pillow.
Cupcake's nose is like a red rose.

Her superpower is that she can fly.
Her other superpower is she can camouflage.
She saves people
And animals that are in danger.
She can even go to Mars
And to the moon.

Lavinia Boloca (8)
Uxendon Manor Primary School, Kenton

Talking Poodle

At night a strange and peculiar pet came to me,
It was hungry so I gave it some breadcrumbs.
After that, it played the drums
But it was time for bed
So we fell into a deep sleep
But before that, the poodle said goodnight to me.

My peculiar pet, my peculiar pet
Has baby-pink, fluffy
And puffy pompoms hanging from its ears
But when it is happy it runs
And jumps in glee.

In the morning my poodle woke me up
And said, "Good morning."
Then we crossed the streets to get something to
eat.
We got the same thing.

Raghavi Nanthakumar (8)
Uxendon Manor Primary School, Kenton

The Big Dog Who Can Make People On Earth Happy

The day I met my peculiar pet it came to me,
I was filled with glee
And so was she.

She was big and fluffy
And had long, smooth hair.
It was curly and whirly,
Just like the air.

The day she came,
The day she came,
The day the big dog came.

She came to me
And said with glee,
"I am the dog who can make people on Earth happy."
She stays with them and plays with them
She fills them with joy and makes them giggle.

The day she came,
The day she came,
The day the big dog came.

Sarah Bizgan (8)
Uxendon Manor Primary School, Kenton

Giraffe In The Woodland

G et up and brush your teeth!

I gloos never keep you warm!

R est in the rubbish dump!

A n apple isn't healthy!

F eet are disgusting!

F un will never end!

E ggs can hatch!

G iraffaroar is a famous animal

I n the peculiar pet zoo.

R ushing through the woodland gate

A s his brown, frizzy hair flies in the wind.

F urry ears to keep him warm and sensitive.

F eeling as snuggly as a lion.

E arly morning, he exercises.

Kieron Choo Fun Young (8)
Uxendon Manor Primary School, Kenton

Boxing Leo

He has big blue eyes,
Quite thick hair like a bear,
Boxing gloves
And big eyes.

He went to the zoo, he wasn't much help,
He snacked on animals' food with some help,
He leapt around and banged his foot,
Now he's in the hospital, look!

He jumps into matches when he is late
Because he is always busy practising near his gate.
He never stops pouncing and boxing
Because he always loves jogging.

This peculiar pet is the best I've ever had
And he's super fab.

Kara Lafond (8)
Uxendon Manor Primary School, Kenton

Harold Made People Annoyed

Harold does not have hair
But does have fur everywhere.
His legs are short but he runs fast.
His knee never hurts when he goes past a tree.
His eyes are black like coal everywhere.

When he plays he starts to beatbox,
Then he starts to beatbox with a fox.
Then he wants to eat a lot,
Then he goes up his Lego blocks
And he smells someone's socks.

When he runs he makes people dizzy,
Then it makes people busy.
When he runs it makes people jiggle,
Does he ever get dizzy or fizzy?

Matthew Andrade (8)
Uxendon Manor Primary School, Kenton

My Pet Cat

The day my cat came to school
She sang a song in every hall.

She sang a song as loud as a big white troll
And every classroom couldn't hear the learning
they were doing.

Also she came into a classroom, she was like a
dragon in the staffroom,
So she went to every classroom, even in the
teacher's staffroom.

Also she made everyone jump, even the teachers
did a big stamp.
Now my cat must go home so she can play with a
bat.

Roseleane Sharma Phuyal (8)
Uxendon Manor Primary School, Kenton

My Cat

My cat is white,
Her eyes shine bright,
She has a little pink nose,
She has long white whiskers,
Sparkle has fluffy ears,
Her fur is as soft as snow.

Ooow!
She is going on an aeroplane.
She is going in the hotel
And it's snowing
And it's cold.

Her superpowers are butterfly wings,
So she can fly like a butterfly.
She has colourful wings like a rainbow
And shines brightly everywhere.

Timeea Ursescu (8)
Uxendon Manor Primary School, Kenton

My Peculiar Pet

My pet likes feet,
He also likes meat.
He goes *sniff, sniff* for my feet.
His eyes are a surprise.
My pet's ears are like tears.

My pet goes *sniff, sniff for my feet.*

My pet likes to play catch
Because he's faster than lightning,
He is faster than a cheetah.

My pet goes *sniff, sniff for my feet.*

Sometimes when he wants to fly
He spreads his wings very wide.

Vera Shlyuger (8)
Uxendon Manor Primary School, Kenton

The Raccoon Superhero

The day he came, my raccoon,
All he ate was bamboo.

His fur was blue
Like my new shoes.

He is a superhero
And he loves the number zero.

His smile is as long as a mile
And his ears look like big tears.

He is a superhero
And he loves the number zero.

He flies and he meets the sky
And he never gives up, he tries.

He is a superhero
And he loves the number zero.

Hanif Mujaddedi (8)
Uxendon Manor Primary School, Kenton

My Peculiar Pet Chicken

My pet chicken likes to fly,
With his boosters in the sky.

After school he went to the hall,
But he was too clever so he played with a ball.

Because my pet chicken is hungry he raided
The lunch hall and paid the lunch lady but she
fainted.

Then it was playtime and he was alone,
So then he turned into stone and got cloned.

But he went to his home
In his little car alone to get combed.

Ayoub Aria (8)
Uxendon Manor Primary School, Kenton

My Peculiar Pet

The day my cat came to school,
She found something and it was wool!

In English she felt sad,
She wanted to go home, really bad!

In science there was an explosion,
It destroyed the school, my cat was in confusion!

She made some friends who were nice,
Then she saw something in the bike shed, it was mice!

My pet cat likes to run
And she has lots of fun!

Anastasia Moisii (8)
Uxendon Manor Primary School, Kenton

My Peculiar Pet Guinea Pig

My pet guinea pig likes to ride,
When she goes down a silver slide.

The day my guinea pig came to school,
She was absolutely cool.

The teacher was no fool,
So she decided to go in the swimming pool.

She gave the children a hint,
She also said, "Have a mint!"

Now my guinea pig must go home,
Before she's going to be all alone.

Sophie Soteriou (8)
Uxendon Manor Primary School, Kenton

My Peculiar Pet Snake

My snake can fly in the sky,
She's a snake, she doesn't know why.

The day my snake came to school,
She munched up the whole school - she was cool.

Her eyes are surprising
And she was scared when she got a prize.

She is rude every year,
Every person says she has a tear.

Now my snake must go home,
But I let her go alone.

Maria Zaghali (8)
Uxendon Manor Primary School, Kenton

My Peculiar Pet

My giraffe loves to glide
And he takes pride.

The day my giraffe came to school
He saw an amazing person, he was so cool.

Then he was almost late for art,
But at the start he made a huge heart.

At last it was time for English,
But she was a bit glitterish.

Finally, it was hometime so he can go home
Before he's alone.

Nadia Celestin (8)
Uxendon Manor Primary School, Kenton

My Peculiar Pet

My fast cheetah loves to race,
Every time he wins there is a grin on his face.

The day my cheetah came to school,
He just acted like a fool.

In maths and English he was bad
Which made him feel very sad.

But in PE he rocked the stage,
No matter of his young age.

Now my cheetah must go home,
so he doesn't stay alone.

Param Parikh (8)
Uxendon Manor Primary School, Kenton

My Peculiar Pet Rabbit

My pet rabbit loves the sea,
He likes to surf with me.

The day my rabbit came to school
He gobbled up the whole school and he was very cool.

My pet rabbit likes to scare,
He has a frightening stare.

My pet rabbit is always mad
And makes everybody sad.

Now my pet rabbit must go home,
Before he is all alone.

Seja Hamid (8)
Uxendon Manor Primary School, Kenton

My Peculiar Pet

My pet leopard likes to run
But it's not fun.

The day my leopard came to school
He wrecked a building and was cool.

He gobbled up the lunch hall
And he took my friend's football.

My leopard is mad
Because he's sad.

He took the ball from the school,
Now he's a fool.

Mekel Charles (8)
Uxendon Manor Primary School, Kenton

The Cat Who Likes To Help

My cat likes to appear
When it hears a cheer.
My cat's eyes look like tears,
He only shows them with his fears.

My cat who likes...
My cat who likes...
My cat who likes to help.

My cat likes to help
With his golden shiny belt.

My cat likes to purr
With his super-soft belt.

Roman Shafiqi (8)
Uxendon Manor Primary School, Kenton

My Peculiar Pet

My hamster likes to sing
And he has a shiny ring.

The day my hamster came to school,
He burnt the classroom, he was cool.

He killed the staff,
It made him laugh.

He drank lots of coffee
But didn't try toffee.

Now my hamster must go home
So he doesn't feel alone.

Irysha Savani (9)
Uxendon Manor Primary School, Kenton

My Peculiar Pet Hamster

My small orange hamster likes to float
Around a muddy moat.

The day my pet came to school
She swam in the place's pool.

It was lunchtime
And it was horrid grime.

She was just a fool
Showing that she is cool.

Now my hamster must go home
Before she is left alone.

Ella Gami (8)
Uxendon Manor Primary School, Kenton

The Cat Who Went In The Park

C ool, cuddly cat.
A s soft as snow.
T errific cat playing all day.

C limbing up trees
A s she went to play in the shade.
T hen she had ice cream.

C ute little cat playing in the park.
A s cute as a puppy.
T hen Katey had fun.

Giulia Elena (8)
Uxendon Manor Primary School, Kenton

My Peculiar Pet

My pet cat loves to sing
With a golden ring.

The day my cat came to school
He munched the big swimming pool.

My cat went on the slide
And had a fun ride.

My cat went on the swing
With his glorious ring.

Now my cat must go home,
Before he is alone.

Sriraam Sivathasan (8)
Uxendon Manor Primary School, Kenton

My Peculiar Raccoon

My peculiar pet is cold like ice.
He likes to play with mice.
My Raccoon likes to drive
In his McClaren prize.
With a Golden chain
Like a favourite plane.
He has cute blue eyes
With a big nose like a gaze.
My Raccoon has a Rolex
With a diamond chain
And a Porsche GT2.

Kamari Cunningham (8)
Uxendon Manor Primary School, Kenton

The Sweet, Cute Coco

D aring and dashing.
O bsessed with balls.
G reat friend, difficult to find.

D reaming and drooly.
O bject of attention.
G orgeous and artistic.

Eliza Maria (8)
Uxendon Manor Primary School, Kenton

My Penguin

My penguin has sparkling eyes.
He sees a star shining in the sky.
He can slide with his big belly.
Sometimes it makes him smelly.
I like my cute penguin
Because he always plays with me.

Zakii-Ali Hussain (9)
Uxendon Manor Primary School, Kenton

My Peculiar Pet

The day I met my snake
He was in a lake.
His tongue was so thin, like a pin
And he smelt like a bin.
He likes to drive for a prize
Until the sun does rise.

Nabeel Alam (9)
Uxendon Manor Primary School, Kenton

YOUNG wRITERS INFORMATION

We hope you have enjoyed reading this book – and that you will continue to in the coming years.

If you're a young writer who enjoys reading and creative writing, or the parent of an enthusiastic poet or story writer, do visit our website **www.youngwriters.co.uk**. Here you will find free competitions, workshops and games, as well as recommended reads, a poetry glossary and our blog. There's lots to keep budding writers motivated to write!

If you would like to order further copies of this book, or any of our other titles, then please give us a call or order via your online account.

Young Writers
Remus House
Coltsfoot Drive
Peterborough
PE2 9BF
(01733) 890066
info@youngwriters.co.uk

Join in the conversation!
Tips, news, giveaways and much more!

 **YoungWritersUK**    **@YoungWritersCW**